Rainy Day Activities
Painting

pages 2–3 on getting started

P9-BZH-071

4 Birds on a Wire

6 Creepy House

8 Slippery Snake

10 Magical Fairy

12 Garden Flowers

14 Friendly Octopus

16 Trees on a Hill

18 Stars in the Sky

20 Pebble Bugs

22 Robot Masks

Getting Started

The projects in this book use lots of art materials that you will already have at home. Any missing materials can be found in craft stores.

brushes

clean water

For some of the projects you will need to use a pair of scissors. Always ask an adult to help you.

paint

paper plates

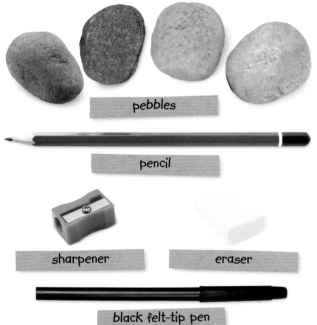

pebbles

pencil

sharpener   eraser

black felt-tip pen

Handy Hint

Acrylic paint has a glossy finish. When the paint is dry it becomes water-resistant, which makes it perfect for many craft projects.

Here is a gallery of all the paper you will need to complete all the painting projects.

Birds on a Wire

To make this picture of birds you will need some blue paper, a black felt-tip pen, paints, and brushes.

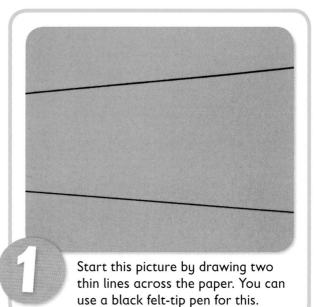

1 Start this picture by drawing two thin lines across the paper. You can use a black felt-tip pen for this.

2 Now paint ovals onto the lines. These ovals will become the birds' bodies. Make them different colors.

3 For the birds' tails use the same color paint to draw triangle shapes coming down from their bodies.

4 When the paint for the bodies has dried, use yellow paint to make small triangles for the birds' beaks.

5 Now use a black felt-tip pen to add some eyes and feet. Draw the birds' feet holding onto the wire.

6 Finish your picture by painting the brown poles that the wires are attached to. Then add more birds!

Creepy House

To make this spooky picture you will need black and white paint, brushes, and orange paper.

1 Start this spooky picture by painting a large black area along the bottom of the paper. This will be the ground.

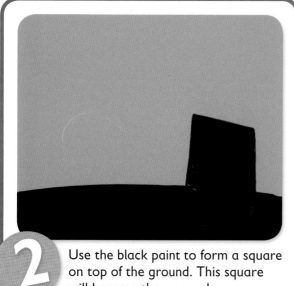

2 Use the black paint to form a square on top of the ground. This square will become the creepy house.

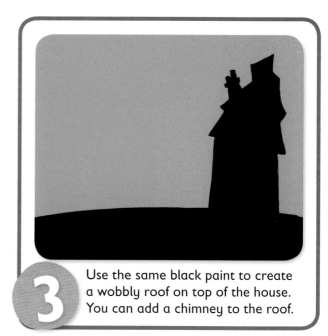

3 Use the same black paint to create a wobbly roof on top of the house. You can add a chimney to the roof.

4 Using the black paint, make the shape of a tree. Paint thin and pointy branches coming off the trunk.

5 Now use some white paint to add the moon in the sky. Also add some windows and a door to the house.

6 To finish this spooky picture you could add some black bats flying in the sky.

Slippery Snake

This snake is easy to create. You will need paper, paints, brushes, and a black felt-tip pen.

1 Start your snake picture by painting a bright green oval on some white paper. This will be the snake's head.

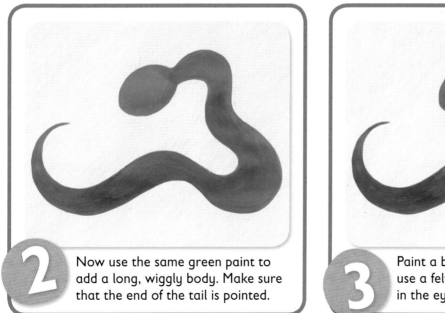

2 Now use the same green paint to add a long, wiggly body. Make sure that the end of the tail is pointed.

3 Paint a big white eye. When it is dry use a felt-tip pen to add a black dot in the eye and a thin black mouth.

4 Now you can begin decorating your snake. Start by painting yellow stripes all the way down the body.

5 Add blue triangles between the stripes. Remember to put a triangle on each side of the snake's body.

6 To finish the snake, add small red dots on the yellow stripes, and white dots in the blue triangles.

Magical Fairy

These cute fairies are fun to create. To make them you need paper, paints, and brushes.

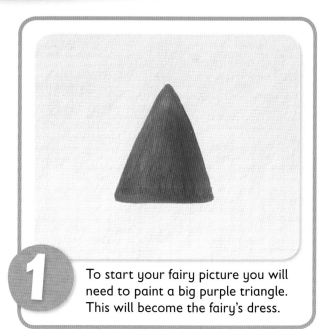

1 To start your fairy picture you will need to paint a big purple triangle. This will become the fairy's dress.

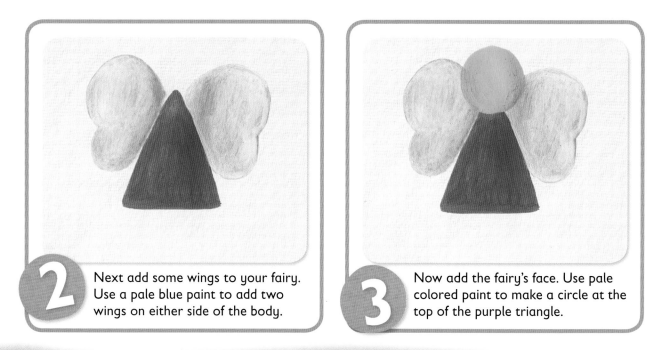

2 Next add some wings to your fairy. Use a pale blue paint to add two wings on either side of the body.

3 Now add the fairy's face. Use pale colored paint to make a circle at the top of the purple triangle.

4 Now paint some dark blue arms and legs onto your fairy. Use brown paint to carefully add some hair.

5 Use some black paint and a thin paint brush to paint eyes and a smiling mouth onto your fairy.

6 You can finish your picture by adding some stars in the sky and giving your fairy a magic wand to hold!

Garden Flowers

To make these pretty garden flowers you will need some white paper, paints, and paint brushes.

1 Start your flower picture by painting a large yellow circle. This will become the center of the flower.

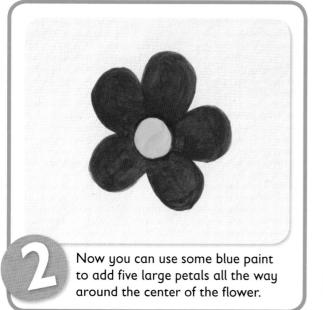

2 Now you can use some blue paint to add five large petals all the way around the center of the flower.

3 Use some green paint to make a stem. The stem should be a line that runs downwards from the flower.

4 Using the same green paint, you should now paint two large green leaves on either side of the stem.

5 You can add some green paint to the ground. This will make your flower look like it is growing on grass.

6 Put the finishing touches to this picture with more flowers, butterflies, and bees.

Friendly Octopus

To make this friendly octopus you will need brushes, paints, a black felt-tip pen, and some blue paper.

1 Start your underwater painting with a large purple circle. This circle will become the body of the octopus.

2 Paint some tentacles coming out of the octopus's body. Try to make them wavy like they are swimming.

3 When the purple paint has dried, use some blue paint to add suckers all along the underside of the tentacles.

4 Now take some white paint and make two large ovals on the body. These ovals will become the eyes.

5 Use a black felt-tip pen to add a big smile onto the octopus. Add some big black circles to his eyes.

6 Finish the picture by painting some seaweed and rocks on the sea floor. You could add some friendly fish too.

Trees on a Hill

To make this picture of trees you will need some white paper, some paints, brushes, and a pencil.

1 You can start your picture by using a pencil to draw three large circles overlapping each other.

2 The circles are a guide for the tree's branches and leaves. Draw the trunk of the tree below the circles.

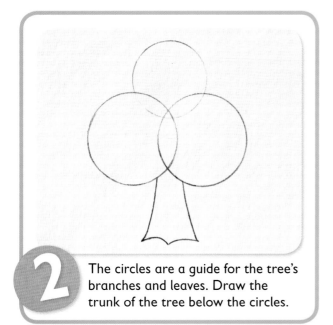

3 Draw wavy lines all the way around the circles. This will make the overall shape of the tree.

4 Use some of your brown paint to color the trunk of the tree. Try to follow the pencil lines carefully.

5 Now use some green paint to color the leaves of the tree. You can also add a blue cloud in the sky.

6 To finish this painting add more trees in different shapes and sizes. Paint more clouds and some grass.

Stars in the Sky

To paint this exciting picture you will need black paper, paints, and some paint brushes.

1 Start your picture by painting some white stars onto the black paper. Make the stars all different sizes.

2 Now you can add a couple of large planets to your picture. Paint a ring around one of the planets.

3 Use white paint to add some small dots around the planets. These are moons that orbit the planets.

4 Now you can add a rocket flying through space. Add some yellow paint for the flames from the jets.

5 You can add a shooting star by painting a small yellow circle and then smudging it with a paintbrush.

6 Ask an adult to help you flick some white paint from a brush onto the paper to make tiny stars.

Pebble Bugs

To make these cute bugs you will need some medium-sized pebbles, paints, and paint brushes.

1 Start by choosing a pebble that is a nice oval shape. Wash the stone and pat it dry with a clean paper towel.

2 Take some red paint and use it to paint the whole pebble. When you have finished, leave it to dry.

3 When the red paint is dry, use black paint to color the end of the stone. This will become the bug's face.

 4 Paint a thin black line along the back of the bug to show the two wings. Now add black dots onto the wings.

5 Paint white circles for eyes onto the face, leave them to dry, and then paint black dots inside the white.

6 You could try using different shaped stones and different colors to create a whole family of bugs.

Robot Masks

To make these fun masks you will need paper plates, paints, and some felt-tip pens.

1 Place a paper plate upside down on a table. Use some silver or gray paint and cover the whole plate.

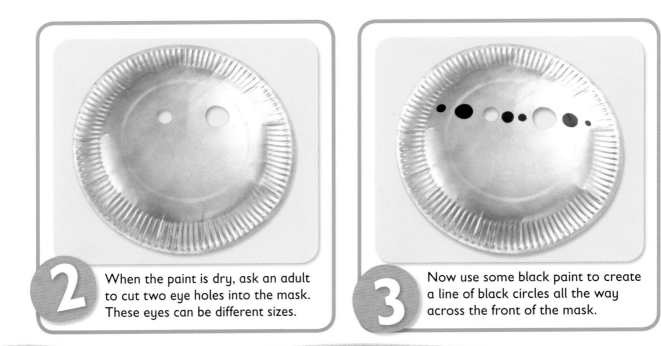

2 When the paint is dry, ask an adult to cut two eye holes into the mask. These eyes can be different sizes.

3 Now use some black paint to create a line of black circles all the way across the front of the mask.

4 Use your black paint to create a large semi-circle mouth. Don't forget to add some teeth to this mouth!

5 You can use more black paint to add a small rectangle in the middle of the plate for the nose of the robot.

6 Try making some more masks for your friends. You can use different colors and designs.

Can you remember?

1 How many *Pebble Bugs* were shown in the final picture?

2 What color paper do you need for the *Stars in the Sky* painting?

3 Which animals are flying around the *Garden Flowers*?

4 What color is the *Slippery Snake's* body?

5 What does the *Friendly Octopus* have on the underside of his tentacles?

Answers on page 96

Rainy Day Activities
Drawing

See pages 26–27 on getting started

28 Happy Faces

30 Squiggly Fish

32 Graffiti Letters

34 In the Country

36 Sailing Away

38 Pretty Butterfly

40 Blasting Off!

42 Simple Buildings

44 Arty Flowers

46 Funny Robots

Getting Started

The projects in this book use lots of art materials that you will already have at home. Any missing materials can be found in craft stores.

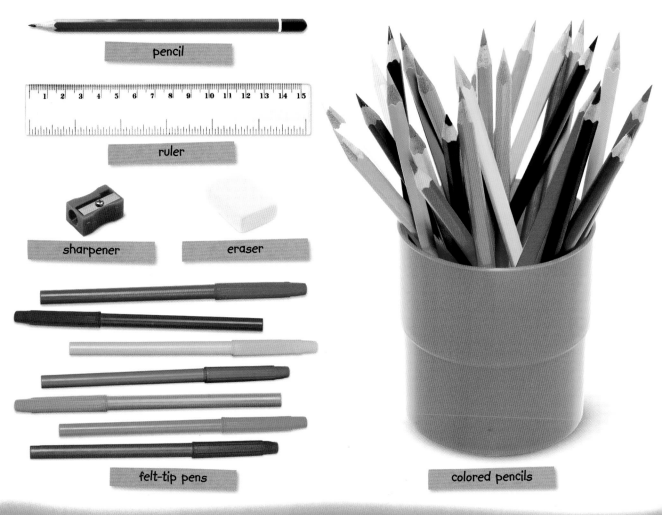

pencil

ruler

sharpener

eraser

felt-tip pens

colored pencils

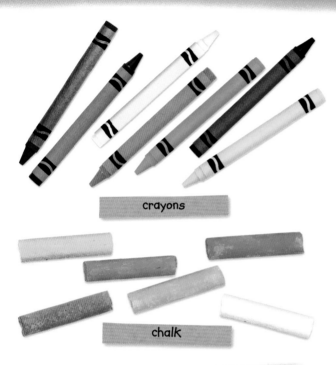

crayons

chalk

Handy Hint

Most of the greatest artists in the world keep sketch books. Try practicing in a sketch book before you start each project.

Here is a gallery of all the paper you will need to complete all the drawing projects.

Happy Faces

To create these happy faces you will need a piece of white paper, a pencil, and an eraser.

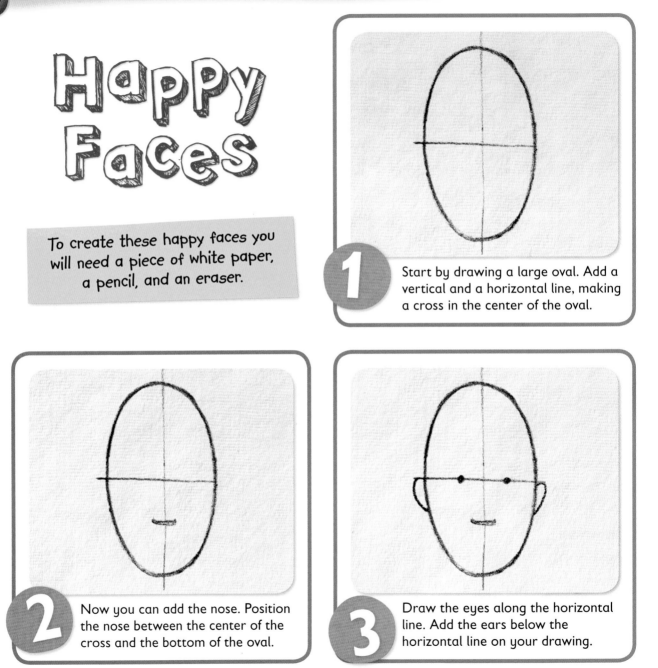

1 Start by drawing a large oval. Add a vertical and a horizontal line, making a cross in the center of the oval.

2 Now you can add the nose. Position the nose between the center of the cross and the bottom of the oval.

3 Draw the eyes along the horizontal line. Add the ears below the horizontal line on your drawing.

4 Now add the mouth to your picture. Draw the mouth halfway between the nose and the bottom of the oval.

5 To finish your face drawing, you can add a hairstyle. Try drawing long hair that is tucked behind the ears.

6 Try using different face shapes and hairstyles. Erase the cross when you are happy with the drawing.

Squiggly Fish

To make this crazy picture you need some paper, some colored pencils, and a black felt-tip pen.

1 Use a pencil to draw wiggly lines all over a piece of paper. Make sure that the lines cross over each other.

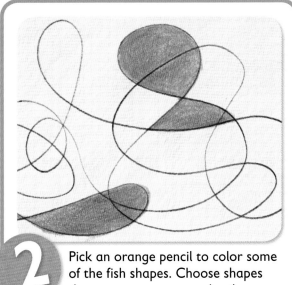

2 Pick an orange pencil to color some of the fish shapes. Choose shapes that are not next to each other.

3 Now use a yellow pencil to color some of the other shapes. Be careful not to color over the lines.

4 Use a blue pencil to color all of the other shapes. The blue area will be the water that the fish swim in.

5 Use a black felt-tip pen to go over the outlines of the orange and yellow shapes. These are the fish.

6 Finish your squiggly fish drawing by using a black felt-tip pen to draw an eye onto each fish.

Graffiti Letters

To make this cool lettering you need some paper, a pencil, an eraser, and some felt-tip pens.

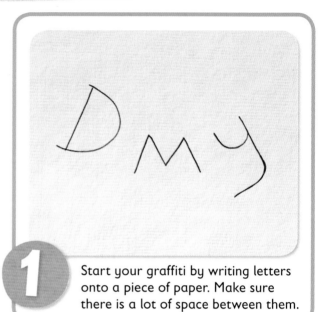

1 Start your graffiti by writing letters onto a piece of paper. Make sure there is a lot of space between them.

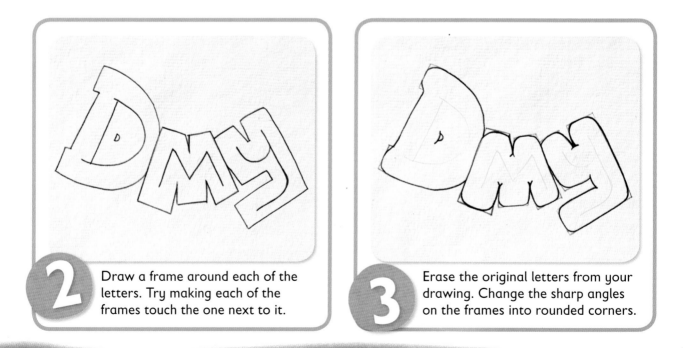

2 Draw a frame around each of the letters. Try making each of the frames touch the one next to it.

3 Erase the original letters from your drawing. Change the sharp angles on the frames into rounded corners.

4 Take a black felt-tip pen and draw around each of the frames. Now add some shading lines inside the frames.

5 Use some of your colored felt-tip pens to add different fun designs inside each of the frames.

6 To finish, draw a border around your graffiti letters with a felt-tip pen. This will help make them stand out.

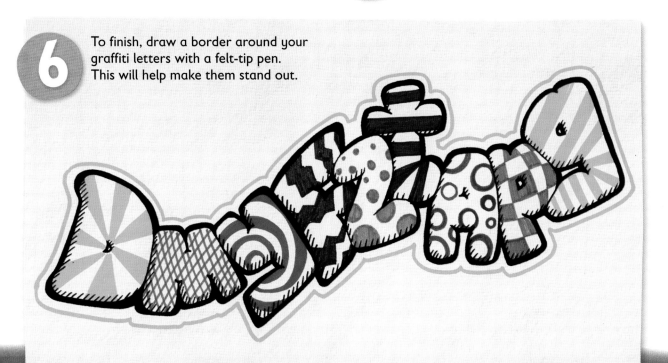

To draw this countryside scene you will need a piece of white paper and lots of colored pencils.

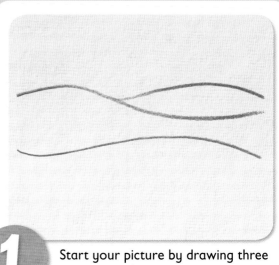

1 Start your picture by drawing three green wavy lines across your paper. These lines will become the hills.

2 Add some trees to your drawing. The trees in the background must be smaller than the ones at the front.

3 Use a gray pencil to draw a road across the hills. Add some marking along the middle of your road.

4 Now add some bushes to your drawing. Color the bushes a darker shade of green than the trees.

5 Add a small pink and purple house on the top of the hill. Now shade the grass in a light green color.

6 Finish your drawing by adding a sun and clouds in the sky, and some flowers onto the grass.

Sailing Away

To make this boating picture you will need some white paper and some colored pencils.

1 To start your picture take a blue pencil and draw a wavy line across the page. This will become the sea.

2 Use a red pencil to draw a boat shape. Don't draw the bottom of the boat as it is hidden in the water.

3 Using a black pencil, draw a big triangle for the sail. Add lines from the sail to the boat for the mast.

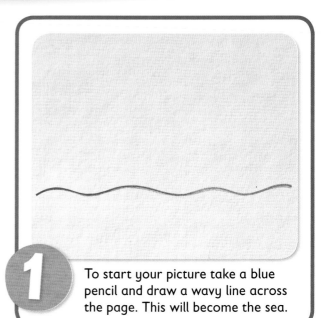
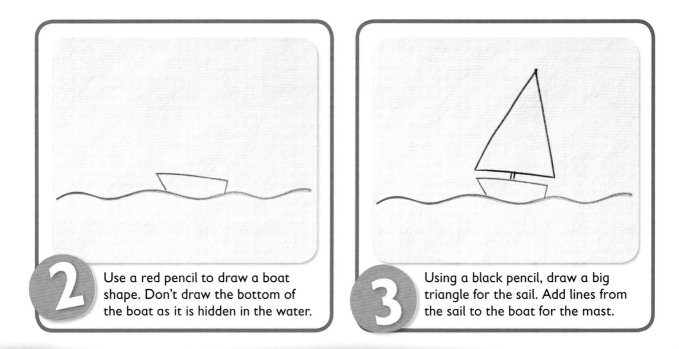

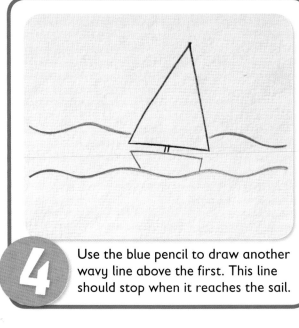

4 Use the blue pencil to draw another wavy line above the first. This line should stop when it reaches the sail.

5 You can add a yellow sun in the sky. Use a black pencil to draw some shapes for birds flying over the sea.

6 Finish by shading in the sea, the boat, and the sun. You could also add some fish swimming in the sea.

Pretty Butterfly

This butterfly is easy to create. All you will need is some blue paper and some crayons.

1 Use a purple crayon to draw a long oval for the body, a circle for the head, and two lines for the antennae.

2 Use a white crayon to draw large wings on each side of the body. Draw some smaller wings beneath.

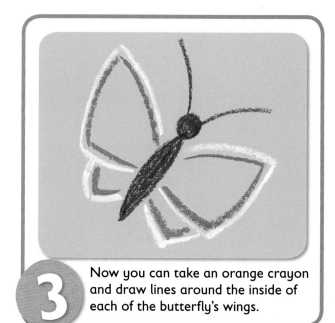

3 Now you can take an orange crayon and draw lines around the inside of each of the butterfly's wings.

4 Use the same orange crayon to draw some dots on the wings. Draw small yellow circles around each dot.

5 Now you can use the white crayon to draw bigger circles around each of the dots on the butterfly's wings.

6 To finish your picture, draw some pretty flowers for the butterfly to flutter around.

Blasting Off!

To make this outer space picture you will need plain black paper and some colored chalks.

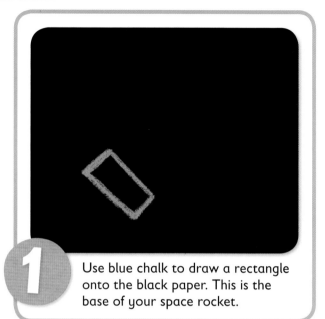

1 Use blue chalk to draw a rectangle onto the black paper. This is the base of your space rocket.

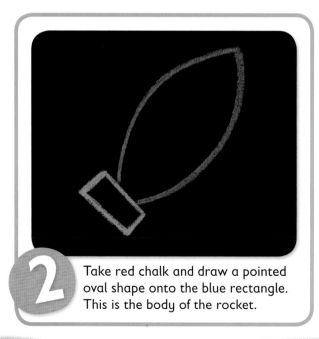

2 Take red chalk and draw a pointed oval shape onto the blue rectangle. This is the body of the rocket.

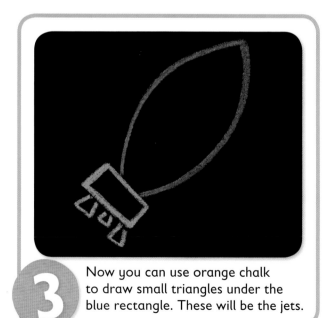

3 Now you can use orange chalk to draw small triangles under the blue rectangle. These will be the jets.

4 Use the orange chalk to color the tip of the rocket and draw three circles for the rocket's windows.

5 To put the finishing touches on your space rocket, use your red chalk to add two wings to the body.

6 Decorate the space background with lots of stars and planets. You can also add some other spacecraft.

Simple Buildings

To make these simple buildings you will need graph paper, some felt-tip pens, and a ruler.

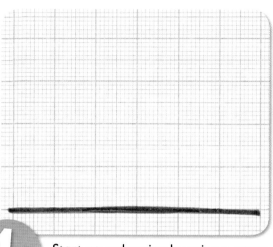

1 Start your drawing by using a green felt-tip pen and a ruler to draw a horizontal line for the ground.

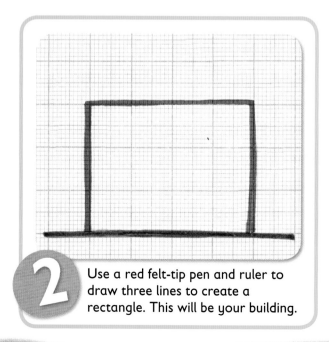

2 Use a red felt-tip pen and ruler to draw three lines to create a rectangle. This will be your building.

3 Add a roof to your building by using a ruler and blue felt-tip pen to draw a triangle on top of the rectangle.

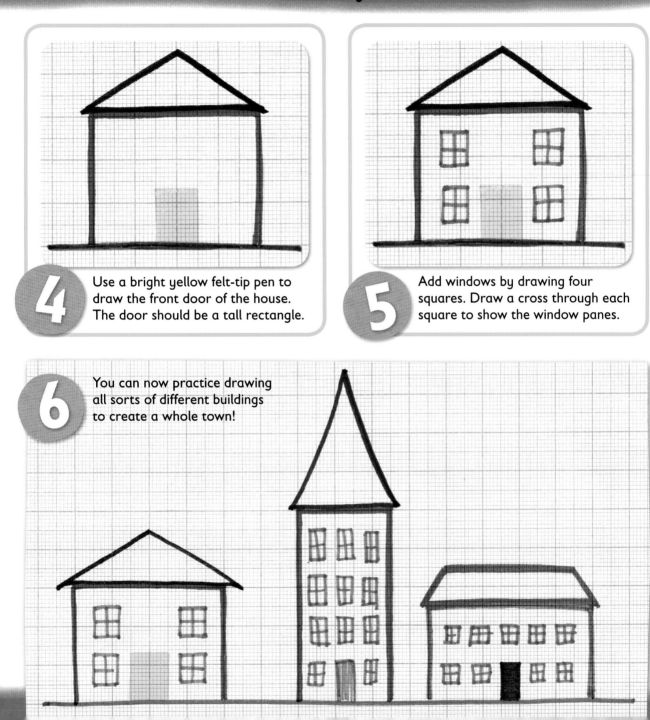

4 Use a bright yellow felt-tip pen to draw the front door of the house. The door should be a tall rectangle.

5 Add windows by drawing four squares. Draw a cross through each square to show the window panes.

6 You can now practice drawing all sorts of different buildings to create a whole town!

Arty Flowers

To create these flowers you will need some colored pencils and a large piece of green paper.

1 Start your drawing by using an orange pencil to draw a small circle. This will be the center of the flower.

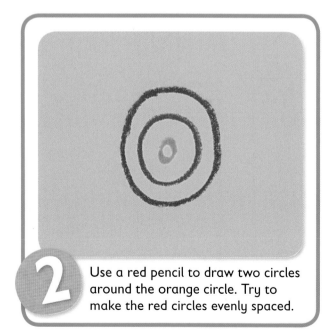

2 Use a red pencil to draw two circles around the orange circle. Try to make the red circles evenly spaced.

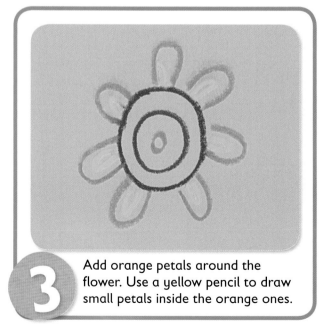

3 Add orange petals around the flower. Use a yellow pencil to draw small petals inside the orange ones.

4 Now add the stem of the flower. Use a green pencil to draw a straight line beneath the flower.

5 Using your green pencil, add leaves to the stem. Try to make each pair of leaves the same size and shape.

6 To finish the picture add a line for the ground and then practice adding flowers in different styles.

Funny Robots

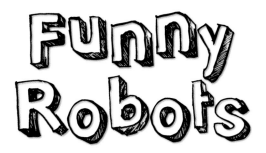

These funny robots are easy to draw. You will need some colored pencils and white paper.

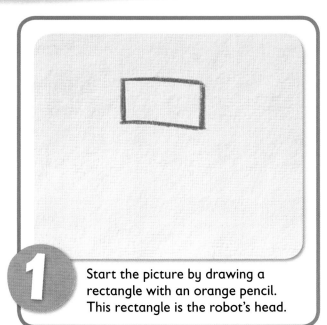

1 Start the picture by drawing a rectangle with an orange pencil. This rectangle is the robot's head.

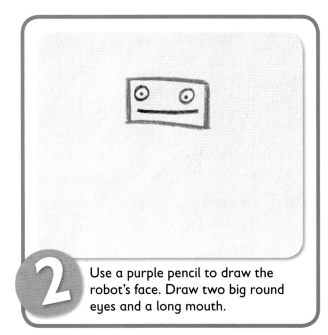

2 Use a purple pencil to draw the robot's face. Draw two big round eyes and a long mouth.

3 Draw an orange four-sided shape for the robot's body. Add the antenna to the top of the head.

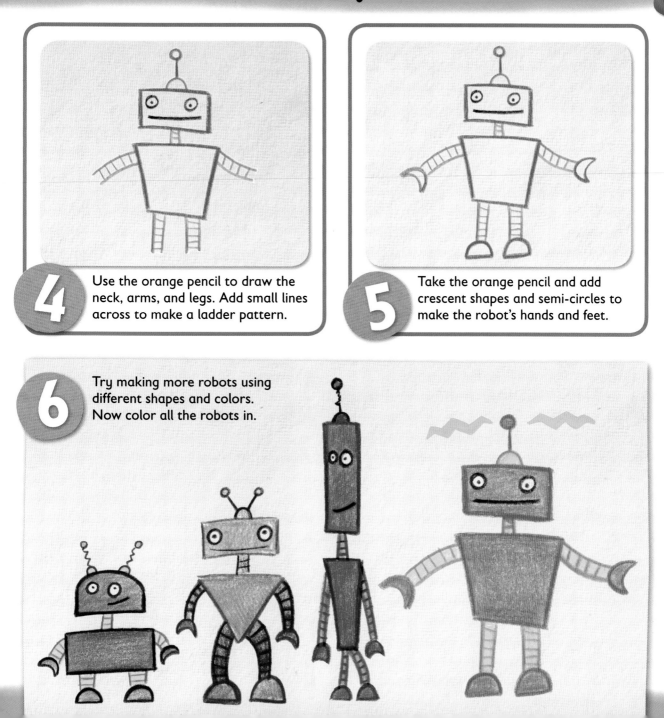

4 Use the orange pencil to draw the neck, arms, and legs. Add small lines across to make a ladder pattern.

5 Take the orange pencil and add crescent shapes and semi-circles to make the robot's hands and feet.

6 Try making more robots using different shapes and colors. Now color all the robots in.

Can you remember?

1 What shape is the sail on the *Sailing Away* drawing?

2 How many windows does the space rocket have on the *Blasting Off* drawing?

3 Which colors are used for the house on the *In the Country* drawing?

4 How many robots are in the final picture of *Funny Robots*?

5 What colors are the fish in the *Squiggly Fish* drawing?

Answers on page 96

Rainy Day Activities
Papercraft

See pages 50–51 on getting started

52 House on a Hill

54 Fancy Fish

56 Time for a Party

58 Papery City

60 Terrific Trees

62 Mighty Mover

64 Monster Mask

66 Funky Cover

68 Arty Frames

70 Garden Flowers

Getting Started

The projects in this book use lots of art materials that you will already have at home. Any missing materials can be found in craft stores.

pencil

ruler

sharpener

eraser

black felt-tip pen

paper plates

old magazines

glue

For some of the projects you will need to use a pair of scissors. Always ask an adult to help you.

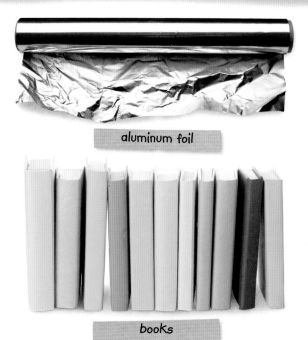

aluminum foil

books

Handy Hint

Wrapping paper, newspaper, or pieces of old wallpaper are excellent for papercraft projects. Why not start a collection?

Here is a selection of the paper you will need to complete all the papercraft projects.

House on a Hill

This pretty house is a fun project to make. You'll need colored paper, glue, and a pair of scissors.

1 Start with a piece of blue paper for the background. Cut a green strip of paper into the shape of bushes.

2 Add some pale green paper under the bushes. The pale green paper will be the grass in your picture.

3 Cut a yellow square for the house and a red triangle for the roof. Now glue all of the pieces down.

4 Cut two rectangles of red paper. Glue one to the roof for a chimney and use the other to make the door.

5 Cut two small squares from some blue paper and glue these onto the front of the house for windows.

6 Add some trees, flowers, grass, and clouds in the sky to finish your picture.

Fancy Fish

To make this exciting underwater picture you will need colored paper, glue, and a pair of scissors.

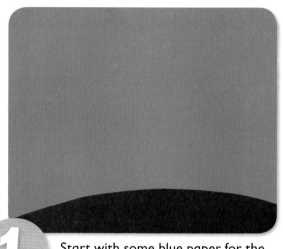

1 Start with some blue paper for the background. Glue some brown paper along the bottom for the sea floor.

2 Cut an oval from orange paper and glue it onto the blue background. This is the body of the fish.

3 Cut some more shapes from the orange paper for the tail and fins. Glue these onto the body.

4 Now use a circle of white paper and smaller circle of black paper to make the eye. Glue them into position.

5 Cut long strips of green paper for reeds in the water. You can add red paper stripes to the body.

6 Finish your picture by adding more fish and gluing blue circles on top for bubbles.

Time for a Party

To make these fun cards you will need card stock, colored paper, felt-tip pens, and scissors.

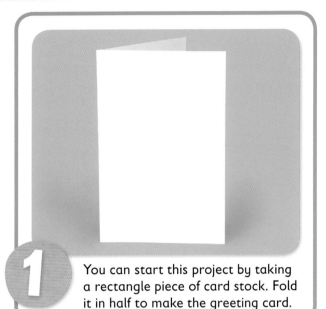

1 You can start this project by taking a rectangle piece of card stock. Fold it in half to make the greeting card.

2 Cut colored balloon shapes from paper and glue them onto the card. Try to have them overlapping.

3 Use a felt-tip pen to draw a wiggly line from each balloon. These lines are the strings tied to the balloons.

4 Now cut two matching strips of paper in the same color. Glue these to the top and bottom of the card.

5 Use a felt-tip pen to write a message on the front of your card. Try to do this in your best handwriting.

6 You can make fun greeting cards for all occasions using this papercraft technique.

Papery City

To make this picture you will need patterned, colored, and graph paper, glue, and a felt-tip pen.

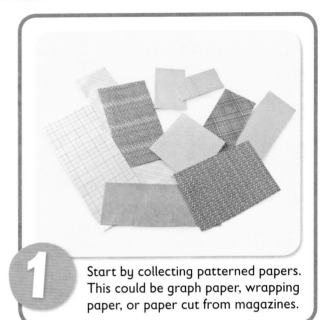

1 Start by collecting patterned papers. This could be graph paper, wrapping paper, or paper cut from magazines.

2 Use a blue sheet of paper for the background. Glue a gray strip of paper to the bottom edge.

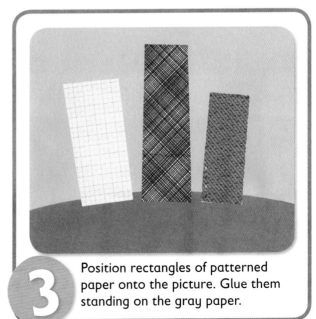

3 Position rectangles of patterned paper onto the picture. Glue them standing on the gray paper.

4 Glue some smaller rectangles in front of the large rectangles. You can now see the city taking shape.

5 Glue some smaller rectangles right at the very front of the picture. These are the smallest buildings.

6 Finish your city by using a felt-tip pen to draw small windows onto each building.

Terrific Trees

This collage uses pictures cut from magazines. To make it, you also need colored paper and glue.

1 Start with a large piece of pale blue paper. Glue a strip of green paper along the bottom for the grass.

2 Cut three rectangles from a brown picture in a magazine. Glue them onto the picture for tree trunks.

3 Use green and yellow pictures cut from magazines to create the leaves of the trees. Glue them into position.

4 Cut grass shapes from a green magazine picture and glue these onto the green paper background.

5 Now you can cut some circles of red paper and glue these onto each of the trees to look like apples.

6 To finish your picture, you could glue some birds in nests onto the tree tops.

Mighty Mover

To make this exciting tractor scene you will need scissors, colored paper, and some glue.

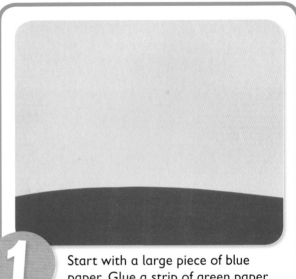

1 Start with a large piece of blue paper. Glue a strip of green paper along the bottom for the grass.

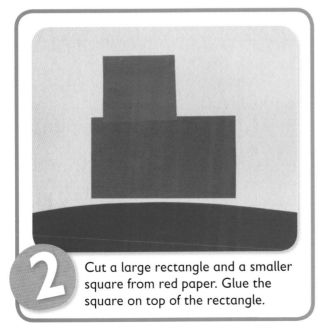

2 Cut a large rectangle and a smaller square from red paper. Glue the square on top of the rectangle.

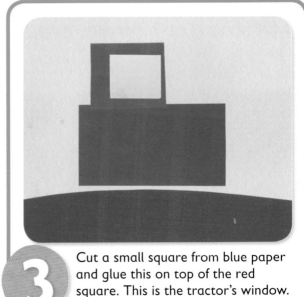

3 Cut a small square from blue paper and glue this on top of the red square. This is the tractor's window.

4 Glue two dark circles of different sizes onto the tractor for wheels. Add smaller light gray circles on top.

5 Add two strips of black paper. One for the roof and the other as the exhaust pipe. Glue them into place.

6 Finish your picture by adding a little sheep, some clouds in the sky, and a barn.

Monster Mask

To make this mask you will need a paper plate, glue, tissue paper, scissors, and a felt-tip pen.

1 Use a felt-tip pen to draw a monster's face onto a paper plate. Remember to add some big fangs!

2 Rip strips of green tissue paper and glue them onto the mask. Make sure that the strips overlap each other.

3 When the mask is covered in tissue paper, use a felt-tip pen to trace over the monster's face so it is bold.

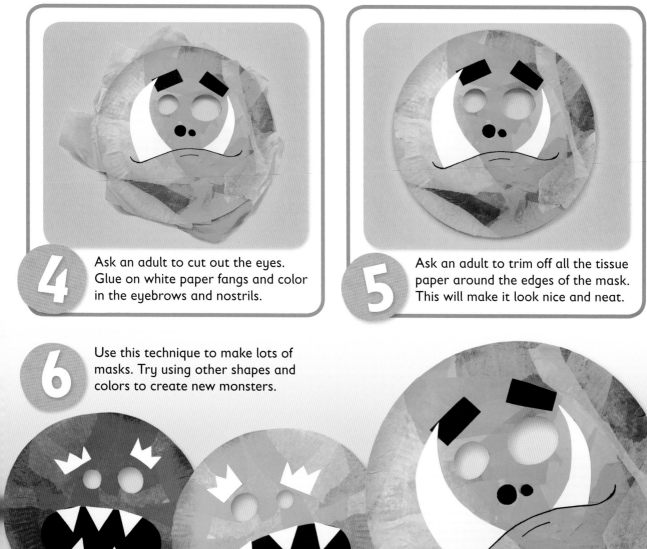

4 Ask an adult to cut out the eyes. Glue on white paper fangs and color in the eyebrows and nostrils.

5 Ask an adult to trim off all the tissue paper around the edges of the mask. This will make it look nice and neat.

6 Use this technique to make lots of masks. Try using other shapes and colors to create new monsters.

Funky Cover

These colorful book covers are fun to make. You will need colored paper, scissors, and glue.

1 Take a large piece of colored paper and cut it into a large rectangle that can be wrapped around your book.

2 Fold the colored paper around the front of the book and tuck the edges inside the front and back cover.

3 Now cut a rectangle from black paper. Make sure that it is slightly smaller than the front of the book.

4 Now you can cut the black rectangle into four separate strips and glue them onto the front of the cover.

5 The next thing to do is to decorate the four stripes. Try using colored triangles to create this zig-zag effect.

 6 Why not design some more book covers? Try gluing circles on top of each other to get a different look.

Arty Frames

To make these arty frames you will need glue, cardboard, colored paper, aluminum foil, and scissors.

1 Cut two rectangles the same size from thick cardboard. Draw a smaller rectangle onto each piece.

2 Ask an adult to cut out the smaller rectangles. This will leave you with two cardboard frame shapes.

3 Cut out shapes of flowers and leaves from the leftover cardboard. You will need four flowers and eight leaves.

4 Glue the frames together and then glue the flowers and leaves on top. Now cover the frame in foil.

5 When the frame is covered in foil you can add colored paper on top of the flowers and leaf shapes.

6 Use this technique to make different frames. You could decorate frames with different colored shapes.

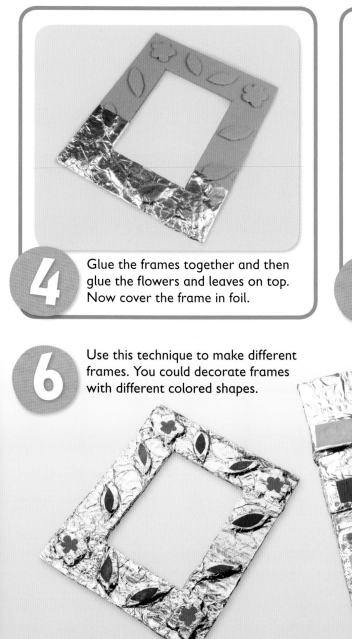

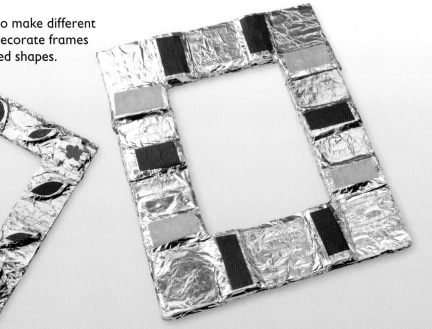

Garden Flowers

This garden flower is easy to make. You will need a pair of scissors, glue, and colored paper.

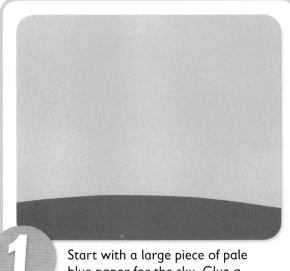

1 Start with a large piece of pale blue paper for the sky. Glue a strip of green paper for the grass.

2 Tear strips of white paper and glue them onto the blue background. They will become clouds in the sky.

3 Cut a thin strip of green paper to make the stem of the flower. Carefully glue this stem into place.

4 Cut five petal shapes from pink paper. Glue each of them on top of the stem to make a flower shape.

5 Glue a yellow paper circle onto the center of the flower. Add two green paper leaves to the base of the stem.

6 To put the finishing touches on your picture, add some other colorful flowers and a ladybug.

Can you remember?

1 How many *Fancy Fish* are in the final picture?

2 What color is the tractor on *Mighty Mover*?

3 What is the *Monster Mask* made from?

4 What pattern does the purple book have on *Funky Cover*?

5 What color is the front door of the *House on a Hill*?

Answers on page 96

Rainy Day Activities
Printing

See pages 74–75 on getting started

76 Swirly Butterfly

78 Potato Paper

80 Spongy Fish

82 Leafy Bookmark

84 Handy Octopus

86 Friendly Bug

88 Bubble Cards

90 Thumb People

92 Eraser Buildings

94 Wriggly Monster

Getting Started

The projects in this book use lots of art materials that you will already have at home. Any missing materials can be found in craft stores.

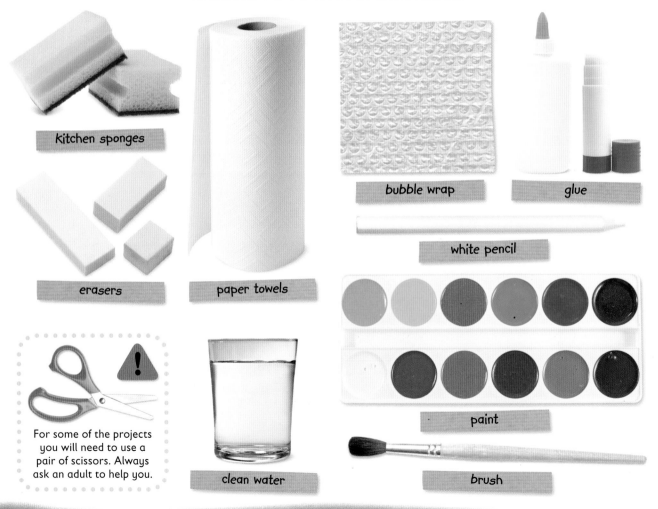

kitchen sponges

bubble wrap

glue

white pencil

erasers

paper towels

For some of the projects you will need to use a pair of scissors. Always ask an adult to help you.

clean water

paint

brush

string

leaves

felt-tip pens

Handy Hint

parsnip

potato

leek

You can create many shapes and patterns
with different types of vegetables.
Experiment with whatever you can find.

Here is a selection
of the paper you will
need to complete all
the printing projects.

Swirly Butterfly

To make these butterflies you need a felt-tip pen, colored paper, paints, water, and a brush.

1 Start by taking a piece of colored craft paper. Fold the paper in half to form a crease, then open it back up.

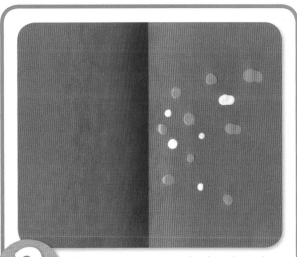

2 Take your paints and a brush and add a few spots and dots of colored paint on one side of the paper.

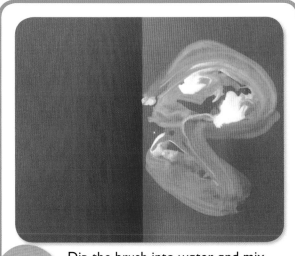

3 Dip the brush into water and mix the paint into a wing shape. Keep the paint on one side of the paper.

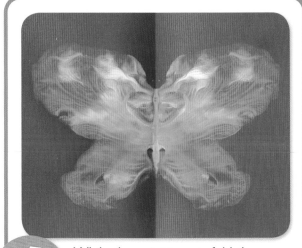

4 While the paint is wet, fold the paper and press down firmly. Open up the paper to see your butterfly!

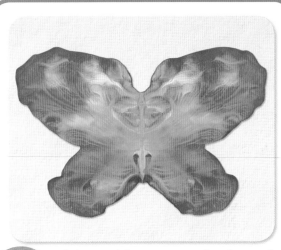

5 Ask an adult to cut out the shape of the butterfly. You can then glue this onto a large white piece of paper.

6 To finish your picture use a black felt-tip pen to draw the body and two antennae onto the butterfly.

Potato Paper

To make this pretty patterned picture you will need paints, paper, and some potatoes.

1 Choose a medium-sized potato. Make sure it is clean by washing it in water. Dry it with paper towels.

2 Ask an adult to cut the potato in half. The two pieces of potato will become your two stamps.

3 Take one stamp and place it flat side down into some orange paint. Place the other stamp into some red paint.

4 Take the orange stamp and carefully press it paint side down onto the top left hand corner of the paper.

5 Now take the other stamp and print next to the first. Do this again until you have filled the whole paper.

6 Make two more stamps with a small potato and print different colors into the original circles.

Spongy Fish

To make this fish picture you will need a kitchen sponge, blue paper, paints, a pen, and scissors.

1 Use a black felt-tip pen to draw the basic outline of a fish onto the base of a clean kitchen sponge.

2 Now you can ask an adult to cut the sponge into the shape of your fish. This will become your stamp.

3 Gently dip the stamp into some white paint. Don't press hard as you don't need much paint on the stamp.

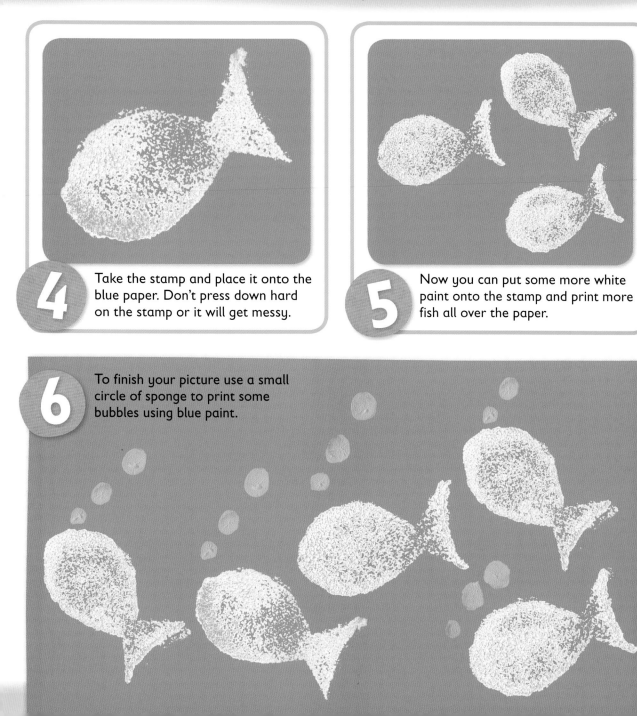

4 Take the stamp and place it onto the blue paper. Don't press down hard on the stamp or it will get messy.

5 Now you can put some more white paint onto the stamp and print more fish all over the paper.

6 To finish your picture use a small circle of sponge to print some bubbles using blue paint.

Leafy Bookmark

To make these leafy bookmarks you will need leaves, card stock, scissors, and some paints.

1 Collect a small selection of leaves. It is a good idea to have leaves of different sizes and shapes.

2 Take brown card stock and cut it into long rectangles. These are your bookmarks ready for decorating.

3 Brush some bright paint onto the underside of a leaf. This is the side of the leaf with ridges and veins on it.

4 Put the leaf paint side down onto the card stock. Press the leaf so that all of it touches the bookmark.

5 Repeat this several times. You can add more paint onto the leaf before pressing it down again.

6 Try experimenting with different paint colors and leaf shapes to make lots of bookmarks.

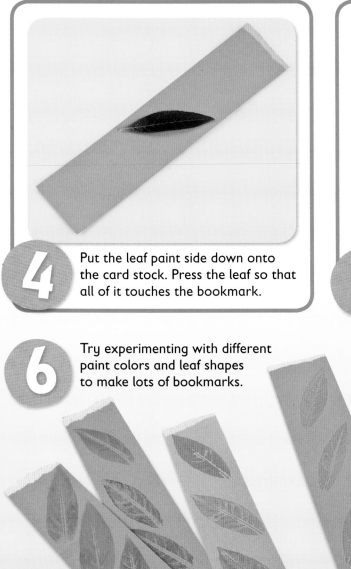

Handy Octopus

All you need to create this octopus is some blue paper, paints, and a black felt-tip pen.

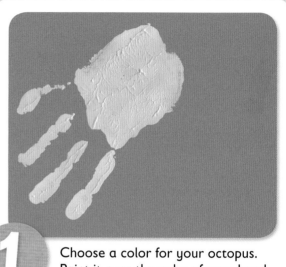

1 Choose a color for your octopus. Paint it over the palm of your hand and press down on some blue paper.

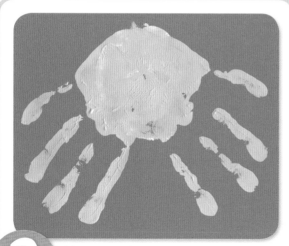

2 Wash the paint off and then paint your other hand. Press it down to make this octopus shape.

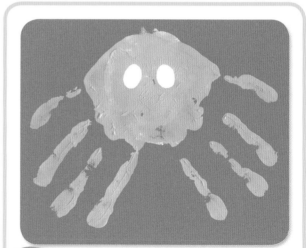

3 When the paint has dried you can use white paint and your fingers to print eyes onto the octopus.

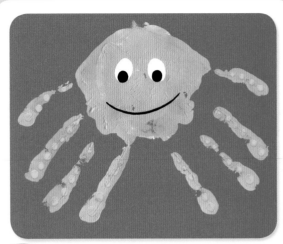

4 When the white paint has dried, use a black felt-tip pen to make a smile. Add some black circles in the eyes.

5 Decorate your octopus by dipping your fingertip in yellow paint and dabbing spots on the tentacles.

6 To finish the picture you could add a few fingerprint fish and then paint some green seaweed.

Friendly Bug

To make this fun caterpillar you will need a kitchen sponge, scissors, paints, and a felt-tip pen.

1 Use a black felt-tip pen to draw a big circle and a small circle onto the the base of a clean kitchen sponge.

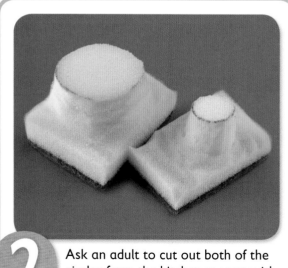

2 Ask an adult to cut out both of the circles from the kitchen sponge with scissors. These are your stamps.

3 Carefully dip the big circle stamp into some green paint and the small circle stamp into yellow paint.

4 Use the stamps to print a wavy line of green circles. Add some yellow circles for the caterpillar's feet.

5 Paint two white eyes. Use a black felt-tip pen to add a smiley mouth and two black circles inside the eyes.

6 When the paint is dry you can use the black felt-tip pen to add some flowers, grass, clouds, and the sun.

Bubble Cards

To make these fun cards you will need paints, card stock, paper, glue, and bubble wrap.

1 You can start this project by cutting a large rectangle shape from a clean piece of plastic bubble wrap.

2 Brush some paint over the bubble wrap. Don't paint the edges of the wrap as this will get messy.

3 Press the bubble wrap down on some colored paper. Remove the wrap to see the printed pattern.

4 Practice this technique with different paper and paint. Try using different combinations to see what you like.

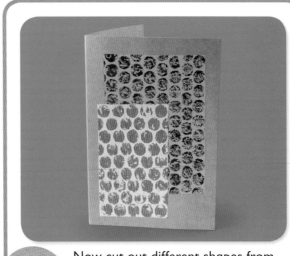

5 Now cut out different shapes from your bubble prints and use them to decorate a greeting card.

6 To finish your card, you could add some decorative paper strips or draw a border with a white pencil.

Thumb People

These thumbprint paintings are fun to make. You will need paper, paint, felt-tip pens, and a thumb!

1 To make the faces. dip your thumb into light-colored paint. Print your thumb a few times on some paper.

2 Wash the paint off your thumb. Now print some brightly colored thumbprints under each original one.

3 Wait until the paint has dried and then use a felt-tip pen to draw a face onto each of the thumbprints.

4 You can now use felt-tip pens to draw different hairstyles onto each of the thumbprint characters.

5 Use the felt-tip pen to draw details onto their clothes and give each character different shoes.

6 You can add more details onto your picture. You could even add some thumbprint animals too.

Eraser Buildings

This project is created by printing with erasers. You will also need paper, paints, and a white pen.

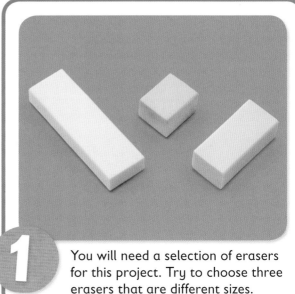

1 You will need a selection of erasers for this project. Try to choose three erasers that are different sizes.

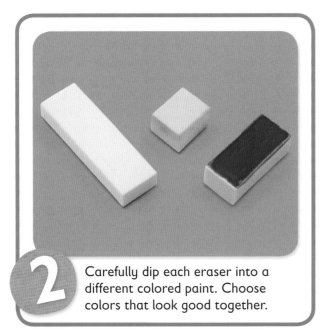

2 Carefully dip each eraser into a different colored paint. Choose colors that look good together.

3 Press the paint side of the eraser down onto some paper. Print three differently colored shapes.

4 When the first three shapes have dried, repeat this until you have lots of differently colored shapes.

5 Now take a white pen and draw windows onto each of the shapes. They now start to look like buildings.

6 To finish your city scene you could add some birds in the sky and some vehicles on the roads.

Wriggly Monster

This monster is fun and messy to make. You will need string, paint, paper, and a felt-tip pen.

1 Start by cutting a length of string. A piece around 10-12 inches will be a good size for you to use.

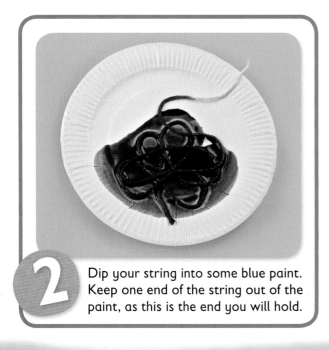

2 Dip your string into some blue paint. Keep one end of the string out of the paint, as this is the end you will hold.

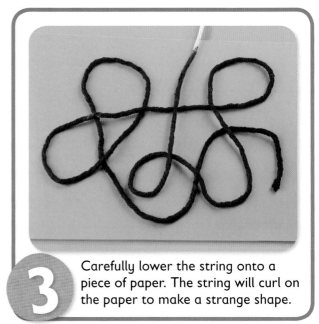

3 Carefully lower the string onto a piece of paper. The string will curl on the paper to make a strange shape.

4 Now you can lift the string off the paper. Turn the paper around to see which way up looks best.

5 Use a felt-tip pen to draw a monster in this shape. Add eyes, feet, fingers, and a mouth. Add a funny hat too!

6 Fill some of the shapes with white paint. Why not make a friend for your monster too?

Answers

Painting

1. four **2**. black **3**. butterflies and bees **4**. green **5**. suckers

Drawing

1. triangle **2**. three **3**. pink and purple **4**. four **5**. orange and yellow

Papercraft

1. three **2**. red **3**. a paper plate **4**. zig-zag **5**. red